# :thelwell's.
# RIDING ACADEMY

FOR
DAVID

# .thelwell's.
# RIDING ACADEMY

METHUEN

**A Methuen Paperback**

THELWELL'S RIDING ACADEMY
ISBN 0 417 01060 5

First published 1965 by Methuen & Co Ltd
First paperback edition published 1969 by Eyre Methuen Ltd
Reprinted five times 1970, 1971, 1972, 1973 and 1975
Magnum edition 1977

This edition published 1982 by Methuen London Ltd
11 New Fetter Lane, London EC4P 4EE
Reprinted 1982, 1984, 1985, 1986 and 1987

Copyright © 1963, 1964 by Norman Thelwell

Made and printed in Great Britain by
Richard Clay Ltd, Bungay, Suffolk

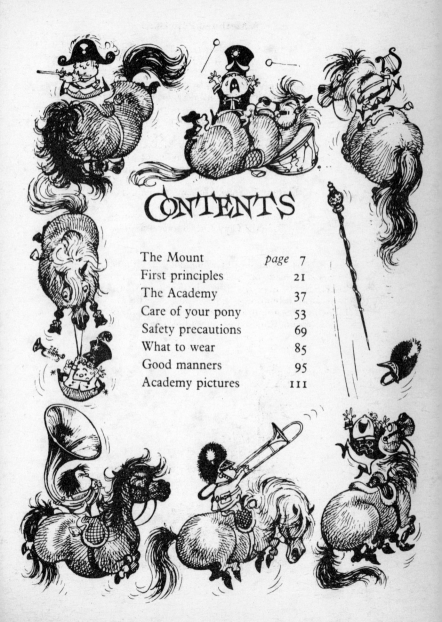

# CONTENTS

'Remember what I told you, girls,
never let him see you're afraid.'

# THE MOUNT

'Do you have one like this in dapple grey?'

Some children discover the joys of
riding at a very early age . . .

. . . others prefer to wait until they are bigger.

Once in the saddle, however, they
are all reluctant to leave it.

Finding a reliable pony is not easy –

professional advice should be sought . . .

Finding a reliable professional
can also have its snags.

You must bear in mind that fat ponies can be hard on the legs . . .

and thin ones hard on the jodhpurs.

Young animals can be unpredictable

and old ones just the reverse.

Some instinct will tell you whether you are going to get on well together.

But *never* buy the first one you see . . .

. . . some day you may want to sell him.

If you buy a pony that is difficult to catch – take plenty of lump sugar with you

and eat as much of it as you can . . .

You will need all the energy you can get.

You may learn a great deal
about a pony by looking
at his teeth

This often applies also . . .

. . . to the rider.

# FIRST PRINCIPLES

'No! No! Deirdre, you've got the wrong foot in that stirrup.'

Most children make very rapid strides as soon as they get into the saddle.

Although steady progress is less easy to maintain –

Mutual respect must be established between pony and rider.

But it should be clearly understood who's boss.

Never speak angrily to your pony.

Use a kind, gentle voice.

It will be just as effective.

Never use spurs –

Do not expect him to be able to read your mind.

Show him exactly what you would like him to do . . .

He'll be very happy to oblige you.

Ponies are very well known for their courage.

But they can be shy, sensitive creatures . . .

So if any obstacle should cause him trouble . . .

... take him back ...

... reassure him ...

. . . and make him do it again.

# THE ACADEMY

'Hand up the one who spotted my deliberate mistake.'

Always get up early when going to riding school – you'll need
plenty of time . . .

. . . to waken your pony.

Don't dawdle on the way . . .

Don't try to be clever . . .

Always enter a riding school by the front gate.

Make friends with the other children.

You will learn a lot from them.

Just sitting on a pony's back is not riding –

so work hard at your studies . . .

There will be plenty of time for play.

Most instructors enjoy a joke . . .

but don't go too far –

Expulsions are difficult for all concerned.

# CARE OF YOUR PONY

'Don't just sit there, dear – hurry home before he catches a chill.'

It is unkind to ride your pony too fast –

Insufficient exercise, however,
can lead to excessive fat.

So give him a good lively trot every day.

The result will astonish you.

Neglecting your pony's coat
is a serious matter . . .

. . . which cannot fail . . .

. . . to cause trouble.

If flies bother him in hot weather . . .

tie a sprig of elder to his brow band . . .

he will find it a great relief.

Your pony's shoes should be checked regularly . . .

Neglect of this simple precaution . . .

can lead to sore feet.

You must learn to recognise signs
that your pony is off colour –

Roaring may indicate wind troubles . . .

. . . and kicking may mean a sore spot . . .

You will know when it's time to call for the vet.

# SAFETY PRECAUTIONS

'What have you done with her *this* time?'

Make sure you know how to pick up his foot . . .

Lack of ability in this direction

may cause you inconvenience.

Never shout 'Gee up'

. . . when teacher is mounting.

Always examine fences carefully
before jumping.

This will enable you to be ready . . .

for any emergency.

Never try out novel ways of
getting into the saddle . . .

you'll enjoy quite enough variety —


— getting out of it.

If accidents are likely to occur . . .

. . . avoid worry . . .

... by making sure that there is a qualified vet in attendance.

Remember that the rules of the road apply to you . . .

as well as to other road users.

All road signs must
be strictly obeyed

and all hand signals
correctly given.

Some riders like to have a lot of
bandages on their horses.

This is not always as pointless . . .

. . . as it may appear.

# WHAT TO WEAR

'I'm breaking in a new pair of boots.'

A smart turnout is
extremely important . . .

A rider's ability can usually be judged

from her appearance.

There is no point in being well
groomed yourself, however,

unless you are prepared to make your pony . . .

. . . look the same.

Roomy jodhpurs are advisable . . .

and a hard hat is a must . . .

Elaborate whips impress nobody – but remember . . .

the most essential item

in a rider's wardrobe

is a good pair of boots.

# GOOD MANNERS

'Don't be so mean, Georgina –
let Christabel have a turn.'

Never let your pony nip other peoples' . . .

It is bad manners for one thing . . .

and can lead to painful results.

The judge's decision must always be accepted as final.

Do not blame your instructor . . .

. . . every time something goes wrong.

Don't play with your pony in the garden –

or allow him into the house.

Don't make fun of other people . . .

. . . you may not be perfect yourself.

You must not expect your mother to keep your pony clean

or your father to give him exercise.

Never forget that winning prizes is not everything . . .

Those who make the odd blunder . . .

are often more popular.

# ACADEMY PICTURES

'You have to approach her slowly and quietly . . .

'. . . holding out a lollipop.'

'It's just a question of which she breaks first, the pony or her neck.'

'You're wasting your time, darlings – you can lead them to
the water . . .

. . . but you can't make them drink.'

'Putting shoes on for you lot is playing old Harry with my eyesight.'

'Next year you can go
pony trekking on your own.'

'They know perfectly well they're supposed to drink
lemonade as a stirrup cup.'

'That was mean – telling her you're engaged to David
Broom.'

'He can manage on tinned food. Why can't you?'

'If I lay my hands on those perishing kids . . .'

'How many trading stamps did
they give you with him?'

'I wish you wouldn't keep hiding them in your bedroom. We'll have the whole house overrun with hounds again.'

'I'm sorry, Mrs Chadwick,
but when your daughter fell
at the double oxer,
I'm afraid she broke a leg.'